The Portal To Gorm

Toby, Jessica, Lucas and Nick might look like ordinary kids, but they're actually superheroes in the magical world of Gorm! As the Lords of Nature, they can control the powers of the Sea, Air, Forest and Earth.

Here in the Primal Pad, the heroes learn their missions from Razzle and jump through the portal to Gorm. The Lords of Nature fight hard to save both Gorm and their own world from being destroyed by Magmion and his evil Volcano Gormiti!

Toby
The Lord of Sea

Toby can blast out water globes and transform his hair into tentacles. His arm changes into a giant lobster claw, and he is a fast and agile swimmer. He has complete control over water!

Age: 13

Personality: Rough and tumble, likes playing pranks on people.

Weakness: His powers boil away like steam if he gets too hot.

Jessica
The Lord of Air

Jessica can fly very quickly and is a skilful mover in the air. She can fire out power blasts and unleash storms on enemies. The edge of her wings cut through rope and rock, and she can throw sharp feathers to pin down bad guys.

Age: 12

Personality: Absent-minded and a bit of a dreamer.

Weakness: She struggles to call her powers if she is underground or in enclosed spaces.

Lucas
The Lord of Forest

Lucas has magical mind powers over plants and some animals. He also has poisonous breath that causes enemies to fall asleep, and an arm that transforms into creeper vines. He can make his feet tunnel underground like roots, and he can also shoot and regrow his wooden fist!

Age: 11

Personality: Always stands up for the underdog, and loves telling jokes.

Weakness: In dry conditions, his plant powers weaken.

Nick
The Lord of Earth

Nick might be slow but he is very strong and can create earthquakes just by punching the ground. His arms and hands transform into stone hammers or rock drills, and he can shoot rock missiles.

Age: 12

Personality: Loves to find out about things but can be a know-it-all.

Weakness: He is so heavy he can't swim – he just sinks like a rock.

Gorm
Land of the Magical Gormiti

Forest Gormiti

Sea Gormiti

Tentaclion
Ancient Guardian of Gorm

Tentaclion is the Elemental Guardian of Sea. This shelled beast, with its huge tentacles, roams the oceans of Gorm. If he grabs hold of a villain, Tentaclion can fling his enemy up to a kilometre away!

Air Gormiti

Volcano Gormiti

Earth Gormiti

Fenision
Ancient Guardian of Gorm

Fenision is the Elemental Guardian of Air. This flying, griffon-like creature hides away and is rarely seen. He is fiercely loyal to the other guardians and the Lords of Nature.

Troncalion
Ancient Guardian of Gorm

Troncalion is the Elemental Guardian of Forest. This lumbering beast walks the lands on four legs and can fire special missiles from its back that explode into tangling vines upon impact.

Roscalion
Ancient Guardian of Gorm

Roscalion is the Elemental Guardian of Earth. This giant beast has a rock mace for a tail and two large stone-horned spikes that can be fired from its head.

Drakkon
Ancient Guardian of Gorm

Drakkon is the Elemental Guardian of Lava. This lava-blasting dragon is the only evil Ancient. Flying on Drakkon's back, Magmion, the Lord of Volcano, can carry out his wicked plans from the skies of Gorm!